NEW KID

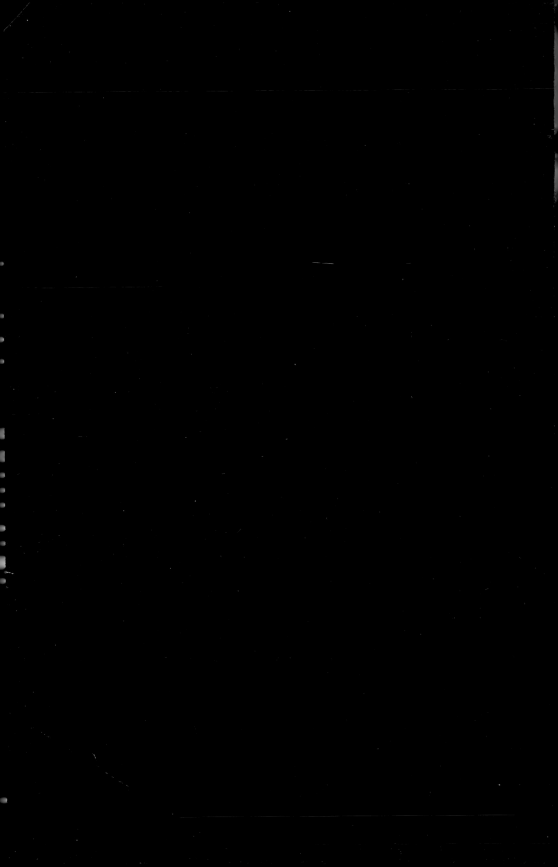

JERRY CRAFT

NEW KID

WITH COLOR BY
JIM CALLAHAN

SCHOLASTIC INC.

ISBN 978-1-338-60089-6

Copyright © 2019 by Jerry Craft. All rights reserved. Published by Scholastic Inc., 557 Broadway, New York, NY 10012, by arrangement with HarperCollins Children's Books, a division of HarperCollins Publishers. SCHOLASTIC and associated logos are trademarks and/or registered trademarks of Scholastic Inc.

12 11 10 9 8 7 6 5 4 3 2 1   19 20 21 22 23 24

Printed in the U.S.A.   23

First Scholastic printing, September 2019

To the Jordan Banks in all of us

I MEAN, I'M NOT **REALLY** FALLING. THAT'S CALLED A METAPHOR. I LEARNED ABOUT THEM IN ENGLISH.

WHEN I WAS YOUNGER I USED TO WISH I WAS **SUPERMAN**. SO INSTEAD OF FALLING, I COULD FLY.

CHAPTER
1
THE WAR OF ART

BUT NOW THAT I'M TWELVE, I REALIZE JUST HOW SILLY THAT WAS.

6

My Dad's Tips for Being a Man!
"Shaking Hands"

The handshake is one of the most important rituals on earth.

Why?

I don't know. Nobody does! But here's how to do it.

step #1 ONLY use your right hand . . . even if you're a lefty.

#2 ALWAYS look each other in the eye!

Good hand

evil hand!!!

#3 Remember, the firmer your grip, the more that people will respect you.

zzz

hmmmm

You're hired!!!

bad

better

best

WHEW!

Chapter

2

The Road to Riverdale

–

There and Back Again

Riverdale

GOOD MORNING.

GOOD MORNING. COME IN.

WELCOME.

AND YOUR NAME IS?

ANDREW ELLIS, MA'AM.

WHOA! SORRY, BRO! THAT NAME IS TAKEN!

BY *ME*!

WELL, NOW THERE ARE TWO OF YOU.

IT'S OKAY, I GO BY DREW ANYWAY.

WELL, HERE I AM . . .

MY VERY FIRST CLASS . . .

AND I ALREADY CAN'T WAIT FOR THIS DAY . . .

. . . TO END!

RRRRRIIIIINNNNNGGGGGGGGGG!!!!!!!!

YOU SURVIVED YOUR FIRST HOMEROOM.

WHAT CLASS DO YOU HAVE NOW?

UMMM . . . PRE-ALGEBRA WITH MR. GARNER.

ANDY SAYS I'M GONNA LIKE HIM.

WOW! YOU'RE *GOOD!*

YOU'RE JORDAN, RIGHT? I'M ALEX FROM HOMEROOM.

CAN I TAKE A LOOK?

HI, ALEX. UMMM . . . OKAY.

HEY, JORDAN. THIS IS RAMON.

HI, JORDAN. WELCOME TO RAD.

THANKS, RAMON!

SORRY TO BREAK UP "THE ISLAND OF MISFIT BOYS . . . "

BUT THIS TABLE IS FOR SOPHOMORES!

YEAH, NOT FOR LOSER FIRST FORMERS!

SO APPARENTLY THERE'S A SEATING ARRANGEMENT!

42

43

J Max Bond Jr Way
HEY, JORDAN!
OH, HEY, KIRK!
YOUR DAD SAID YOU'D BE HOME AROUND NOW.
SO WHAT'S BEEN UP?
JUST BUMMED ABOUT MY NEW SCHOOL.
YEAH, I FIGURED. I KNOW TH-
OH . . .
I'LL CATCH YOU LATER, JORDAN.
'KAY, SEE YA.
WHO'S THAT?
UMM . . . JUST A FRIEND FROM THE BLOCK.

51

I AM BATMAN!

FREAK!

HI, MR. AND MRS. NORTH.

HI, JORDAN.

Jordan's Tips for Taking the Bus

Fitting in on the ride to school is hard work!
I have to be like a chameleon.
For example, in Washington Heights,
I try to look tough.

Inwood is a little different, so I can lose the hood.
No one ever smiles in the morning, so you won't catch
me doing that either!

Kingsbridge is where all of the public school kids get off,
so it's okay to take off my shades. I can even draw!

Last comes Riverdale, where I do my best not to look cool AT ALL! No shades, and definitely no hood. I don't even like to draw 'cause people might think I'm going to use my markers to "tag the bus"!

I LOVE quadratic equations, don't you?

Man! By the time I get to school, I'm exhausted!!!

That new kid is kinda cool.

Yet so non-threatening!

Jordan Banks

HEY, MR. "I-DRIVE-TO-SCHOOL-IN-A-FANCY-CAR-WHILE-OTHER-PEOPLE-HAVE-TO-TAKE-THE-STINKY-BUS."

IT'S *NOT* THAT FANCY, OKAY?!

SORRY, DUDE, I WAS ONLY JOKING!

MY BAD, JORDAN. MY MOM ALWAYS STRESSES OUT WHEN MY DAD IS GONE.

DOES YOUR DAD TRAVEL A LOT, TOO?

NAH, HE RUNS THE COMMUNITY CENTER A FEW BLOCKS FROM OUR HOUSE.

SO HE'S ALWAYS CLOSE BY.

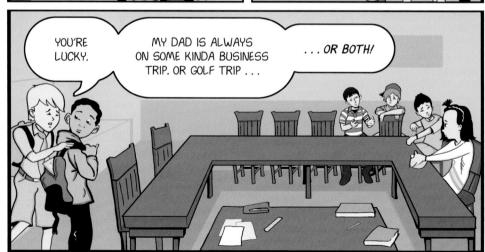

YOU'RE LUCKY.

MY DAD IS ALWAYS ON SOME KINDA BUSINESS TRIP. OR GOLF TRIP . . .

. . . OR BOTH!

RRRRRIIIINNNNNGGGGGGGGGG!!!!!!!!

RRRRRIIIIINNNNNGGGGGGGGGGG!!!!!!!!

Jordan's Guide to Fall Sports

First of all, our team name is *The Riverdale Academy TadPoles*, or *The RAD Tads!* Ugh!

BRAD THE RAD TAD

This semester, everyone has to Join a team or Go out for the musical. I can't sing!

I thought about football, but then I thought about this!

JORDAN BANKS "IDIOT" BORN 20__ DIED VIOLENTLY

My other choices are cross-country, volleyball, competitive yoga, ultimate Frisbee (no Joke), and soccer.

Even though I've never Played before, Liam told me that all I needed to make one of our five soccer teams is a couple of these:

Team 1: Varsity

Team 2: Junior Varsity

Team 3: Thirds

Team 4: Lower Form A Team

Team 5: Lower Form B Team

Guess which one I made.

They even made me captain because I'm the only kid who NEVER threw up during practice AND has never had a concussion.

Now, the varsity games are amazing! Players soar high into the air to make acrobatic kicks!

And parents pack the stands to cheer for their kids.

YES! SCORE!!!

Meanwhile, *OUR* games look more like they're casting for a low-budget karate movie.

Parents use the time to check email or play *Words with Friends.*

YES! TRIPLE WORD SCORE!!!

Jordan Banks

CHAPTER 6

JORDAN BANKS:
THE NON-WINTER SOLDIER

HEY, J, WE'RE HOME.

HOW WAS IT?

JORDAN BANKS! A C IN SPANISH?

SORRY, MOM. ST. HARWELL'S NEVER TAUGHT US THE VOSOTROS FORM.

BUT I GOT IT NOW.

GO AHEAD. ASK HIM, CHUCK.

GIVE ME A CHANCE.

EVERYTHING OKAY, DAD?

THAT'S WHAT I WANTED TO ASK YOU.

YEAH, FINE . . . I THINK.

IT'S JUST THAT . . .

UH-OH.

WHO WANTS TO SIT IN THE GRASS WHEN IT'S *FREEZING* OUTSIDE?

SO . . . UMMM . . . WHAT DID MY OTHER TEACHERS SAY?

I TOOK NOTES. MS. BROSNAN SAID YOU HAND IN YOUR WORK ON TIME AND ARE DOING WELL.

MS. RAWLE SAYS YOU'RE VERY WELL-SPOKEN AND WELL-BEHAVED.

WHICH *WOULD* BE A COMPLIMENT IF YOU WERE IN *KINDERGARTEN*.

MR. GARNER SAID YOU'RE DOING WELL IN PRE-ALGEBRA.

ALEXANDRA'S MOMMY AND DADDY SAID THAT YOU WANT TO BE OUR FRIEND.

WE WOULD LIKE THAT A *LOT!*

WAIT... WHAT?... NO... THEY... SAID... THEY... TALKED... TO... ALEX'S... PARENTS...

NO, SILLY BILLY. MY MOM AND DAD CALL ME ALEX AT HOME.

GASP!!! MY PARENTS DIDN'T TELL *ALEX'S* PARENTS HOW MUCH I LIKE *HIM!*...

THEY TOLD *ALEXANDRA'S* PARENTS HOW MUCH I LIKE *HER!!!*

WONK!!!

THEY SAY THAT THERE ARE SOME ANIMALS THAT WILL CHEW OFF THEIR OWN LEG TO GET OUT OF A TRAP. I NEVER UNDERSTOOD THAT...

UNTIL NOW!

THEN I THOUGHT OF MY GRAN'PA WHO SAYS, "YOU DON'T HAVE TO LIKE EVERYONE, BUT YOU DON'T HAVE TO BE A JERK ABOUT IT, EITHER!"

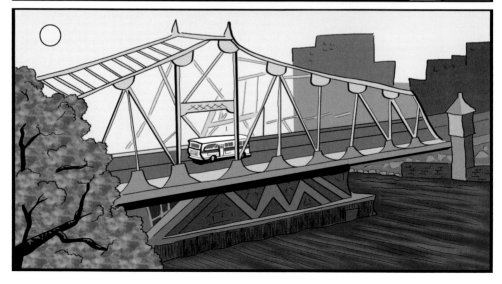

CHAPTER 7

THE CHINESE FOOD
CONNECTION

THANKSGIVING BREAK: WHEN I WOKE UP ON SATURDAY, I COULDN'T STOP THINKING ABOUT MY GRAN'PA. AND THEN . . .

HIYA, KIDDO!

GROW ALREADY!!!

GRAN'PA!

I WAS *JUST* THINKING ABOUT YOU.

AND I WAS THINKING ABOUT YOU, TOO.

SO ARE YOU SIX FEET TALL, YET?

I *WISH!* . . .

SO . . . HOW ARE YOU?

I MEAN . . . ARE YOU HAPPY WHERE YOU ARE?

ABSOLUTELY! IT'S SO QUIET AND PEACEFUL. I'M SORRY I LEFT, BUT IT WAS TIME FOR ME TO MOVE ON.

JUST KNOW THAT I'M IN A MUCH BETTER PLACE NOW.

(SIGH) I'M GLAD . . .

BUT I'M SAD, TOO, BECAUSE YOU . . . YOU . . .

YOU . . . YOU KNOW . . .

111

Taking Photos with My Mom
A Tale of Terror!

First, my mom can NEVER find her camera. It could be anywhere!

behind potato salad

Plus, it's really old! It used to be her dad's so she refuses to get a new one or use her phone. It still uses something called film! Google it!

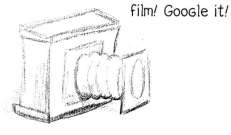

Then she makes us take a *jillion* shots in hopes that a few of them might *actually* turn out good.

But they almost never do!

Furman Craser

Then it's HER TURN to pose for a *Jillion* pics.
Sometimes she even changes her clothes between shots.
And shes ALWAYS asks a Jillion questions.

Were my eyes open?

Was I smiling?

How do I look?

And this is how THOSE come out . . .

Eyes closed

NO smile

No comment

But the worst part is that by the time she gets her photos developed (that's right, developed!) and sees how BAD they are, it's usually too late to do anything.

oh no!

PHOTOS

Wait, Chuck. Bring the tree back inside, we have to retake our Christmas photos!

The end

Jordan Banks

CHAPTER 8

STRAIGHT
OUTTA
SOUTH
UPTOWN

Judging Kids by the Covers of Their Books!

MAINSTREAM BOOKS

AFRICAN AMERICAN BOOKS

MAINSTREAM BOOK COVERS:

Cool, colorful illustrations full of magic and hope!

MAINSTREAM BOOK PLOTS:

Prince Aimii leaves his dull life to slay a dragon, rescue Princess Brea, and prove to his father that one day he'll make a worthy king.

AFRICAN AMERICAN BOOK COVERS:

A depressing photograph full of realism and hopelessness.

AFRICAN AMERICAN BOOK PLOTS:

After moving to his third city in three years, DaQuell "Scooter" Jackson must decide if he will pursue his dream of being in the NBA or join a notorious gang.

MAINSTREAM BOOK HEROES:

* Lives in a magical kingdom!

* Lives in a stable home!

* Wants to live better!

* His father is king!

REVIEWS:

A thrilling magical tale that is sure to inspire readers of all ages to never give up until they have found the treasure they seek.

—School Library Journal

AFRICAN AMERICAN BOOK HEROES:

* Lives in the hood!

* Lives in a broken home!

* Just wants to live!

* His father is gone!

REVIEWS:

A gritty, urban reminder of the grit of today's urban grittiness.

—Jet magazine

Jordan Banks

SECRET SANTA: DAY ONE

OOOOHHHHHH!

CHECK IT OUT! BROWNIES.

YUM!

BEATS MY BROKEN CANDY CANES!

WHAT DID YOU GET, DREW?

GIANT COOKIES . . .

IN THE SHAPE OF BASKETBALLS!

NICE . . . I THINK.

134

CHAPTER 9

A KWANZAA STORY

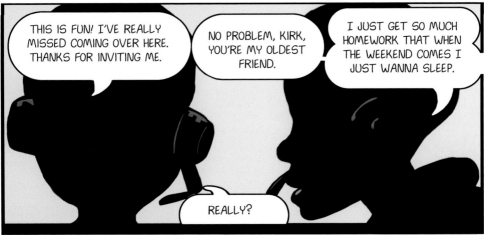

I GOT IT. I GOT IT! I TOLD YOU, YOU DON'T HAVE TO GET THE DOOR!

IS HE TALKING TO HIS *MOM* LIKE THAT?

DING DONG

HI, JORDAN! THANKS FOR COMING! HI, MR. BANKS.

WHAT TIME SHOULD I PICK YOU UP, J?

OH, DON'T WORRY ABOUT THAT, SIR, WE'LL MAKE SURE HE GETS HOME.

OH . . . OKAY . . . WELL . . . HAVE FUN, GUYS.

LOSER!

DAD?

YEAH?

THANKS FOR EVERYTHING. YOU'RE THE BEST!

149

BYE, MRS. LANDERS.

BYE, DEAR. COME BACK ANY TIME.

SO . . . ARE WE STILL COOL?

YEAH, WHY WOULDN'T WE BE?

AWESOME! MERRY CHRISTMAS, JORDAN! THIS IS FOR YOU.

WOW. THANKS!

BUT I DON'T HAVE ANYTHING FOR YOU.

YOU'RE MY FRIEND.

THAT'S A LOT!

▸▸ X-MAS DAY. THERE REALLY ISN'T MUCH THAT I WANT. BESIDES THE NEW *NBA 2K*!
NBA 2K
E
BUT I KNOW IT'S TOO EXPENSIVE. I CAN **NEVER** GET GAMES UNTIL THEY DROP BELOW FIFTY DOLLARS.
BLOOD AND GORE
GORE AND BLOOD
OOOH! PAC-MAN!
CHEAP-O BIN
EVEN CHEAPER
WHICH IS WHY I'M ALWAYS SO FAR BEHIND ON MADDEN.
DAD, WHO'S JOE NAMATH AGAIN?
PRE-ORDER NOW!
BUT WHAT I **REALLY** WANTED, NO ONE COULD GIVE ME . . . ***A GROWTH SPURT!*** THAT WOULD BE ***AWESOME!***
WOW! THANKS, GUYS!
TRY IT ON, SON.
LOOK, I'M 6'4"!

POINT GAME, **LOSERS!**

C'MON, FELLAS, WE'RE PLAYING TERRIBLE!

ACTUALLY, YOU'RE PLAYING TERRI*BLY*.

THE SOCKY HORROR PICTURE SHOW

PICTURE SHOW

CHAPTER 10

GOOD AFTERNOON, I'M ASHLEY MARTIN AND WELCOME TO THE *RAD VACATION REVIEW*...

A LOOK AT THE WINNERS AND LOSERS DURING OUR HOLIDAY BREAK.

THE BIGGEST WINNER HAD TO BE CINDY MARCUS, WHOSE DAD CHARTERED THE SPACE SHUTTLE TO RING IN THE NEW YEAR IN ORBIT.

HER VACATION WAS LITERALLY "OUT OF THIS WORLD"!

ROBBY D. WAS A CLOSE SECOND. HIS FAMILY SPENT CHRISTMAS WITH HIS HOLINESS THE POPE!

AHHH... ROME SWEET ROME!

MEANWHILE, ANDY WENT TO HAWAII WITH HIS TRUSTY MINION COLLIN. "THANK GOODNESS WE DIDN'T GO TO HAWAII!," SAID *EVERYONE!*

VACATION LOSERS INCLUDE JORDAN, DREW, MAURY, ALEX, RAMON, AND THAT CREEPY PUPPET GIRL.

ACTUALLY, WE WENT TO OUR VILLA IN TUSCANY.

I STAND CORRECTED.

AND NOW, LET THE TANNING CONTEST BEGIN!

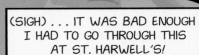

LOOK, JORDAN, I'M EVEN DARKER THAN *YOU!*

(SIGH) . . . IT WAS BAD ENOUGH I HAD TO GO THROUGH THIS AT ST. HARWELL'S!

BUT THIS FEELS EVEN WORSE.

FLASHBACK

HEY! CHECK IT OUT, EVEN MY WHEAT BREAD IS DARKER THAN JORDAN.

AND IT'S NOT EVEN TOASTED!

C'MON, MAN, I'LL BUY YOU A FREE LUNCH.

177

▸▸ AFTER MATH CLASS

THAT WAS *SOOOO COLD!* BUT AWESOME!

HE DESERVED IT.

TRUE.

GOTTA RUN, MY DAD IS PICKING ME UP.

UP FOR A LITTLE *CALL OF DUTY* WITH LIAM LATER?

SURE, I CAN PLAY FOR A BIT AROUND SEVEN.

BUT JUST FOR A GAME OR TWO, THEN I GOTTA STUDY.

COOL! CATCH YA LATER.

THIS IS WHERE YOU'RE SUPPOSED TO TELL ME THAT NO ONE REALLY THINKS I'M WEIRD.

EVEN THOUGH THEY REALLY DO.

OH . . . SORRY, ALEX. MY GRAN'PA ALWAYS SAYS "NEVER COMFORT SOMEONE WITH A LIE."

DON'T BE SORRY, JORDAN. I RESPECT YOUR HONESTY.

OH, HERE!

THANKS.

SO THERE I WAS, IN THE RAIN, TALKING TO THE WEIRDEST KID IN MY GRADE. MAYBE EVEN THE *WHOLE SCHOOL* . . .

. . . HOPING WITH ALL MY MIGHT THAT MAYBE SHE'S NOT AS WEIRD AS EVERYONE *THINKS* SHE IS. AND *MAYBE* SHE'LL STOP CARRYING AROUND THOSE STUPID PUPPETS. AND STOP TALKING IN THAT ANNOYING PUPPET VOICE SO PEOPLE WOULD SEE HOW NICE SHE IS.

BUT DEEP DOWN, WHAT I WAS HOPING FOR MOST OF ALL . . . AND I MEAN *REALLY* HOPING WITH ALL MY MIGHT . . .

OH . . . ACTUALLY IT'S NOT THAT BAD. I REALLY DON'T THINK ANYONE WILL TEASE YOU ABOUT IT, ALEX.

REALLY?

HEY, IT'S OUR PARENTS.

PROMISE NOT TO TELL?

BUT WHY? YOU SAVED YOUR LITTLE BROTHER. YOU'RE A **HERO**!!!

WELL . . . OKAY, YOU CAN TELL **ONE** PERSON.

DEAL!

BYEEE, JOR-DANN!

OOPS! DIDN'T MEAN TO DO THE PUPPET VOICE.

SORRY I'M LATE. HOW WAS YOUR DAY?

WHERE DO I START?

CHAPTER 11

FIELD OF SCREAMS

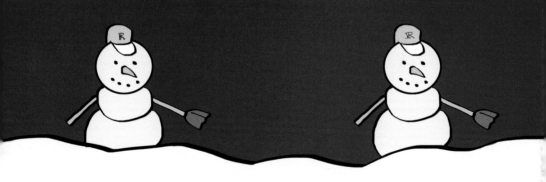

The Baseball Hall of Shame!

When spring came we had the choice of baseball, crew, tennis, fencing, and some sport where you catch a ball with a net on a stick. That looked really hard.

I've never played any of those sports in real life, but at least I knew the rules from playing Major League Baseball 2K6 on Xbox. And watching games on TV.

my dad

2K6
1987

CHEAP-O BIN

For once, Drew didn't know how to play any of those sports either. Mainly because where he lives, there are even fewer parks than where I live.

Park!

The good news is that they put us on the same team. The bad news is that since so many kids went out for the *net-on-a-stick* game, they only had enough players for one lower-form baseball team.
That meant Andy was on our team, too!

TADS   TADS

Then we found out why so few kids go out for baseball. His name is Coach Jim Bumdoody!

First of all, how can you not laugh at a name that has both "bum" and "doody" in it?

I'll tell you how: because rumor has it that some "hot dog" (that's what they call show-offs) made that mistake back in 1997.

And the coach ate him while his horrified team watched. I mean literally, too. Swallowed him whole!

That was one hot dog that didn't even need mustard.

A Public Service Announcement

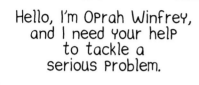

Hello, I'm Oprah Winfrey, and I need your help to tackle a serious problem.

Because there's something going around your school and you may not even know about it.

Something bad!!!

And the worst part is that some of your own friends may be on it.

What are they on?

REFRIGERATOR

WHAT?!! WHY IS EVERYONE ALWAYS SO SENSITIVE ABOUT EVERYTHING?

BESIDES, I'M NOT EVEN TALKING TO YOU, **DREW!**

ME AND RAMON ARE COOL.

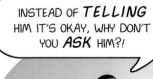

INSTEAD OF **TELLING** HIM IT'S OKAY, WHY DON'T YOU **ASK** HIM?!

RELAX, DAWG, I WAS ONLY BEING—

AND AT THAT
MOMENT, IT
ALL BECAME
TOO MUCH!

TOO MUCH OF KIDS
LIKE ME TRYING
TO FIT IN.

TOO MUCH OF KIDS WHO
SHOULD FIT IN TRYING
HARD NOT TO.

TOO MUCH OF GOOD KIDS
BEING BLAMED FOR
BEING BAD!

TOO MUCH OF BAD
KIDS GETTING
REWARDED FOR THEIR
MEAN BEHAVIOR!

AND WAYYYY
TOO MUCH
OF ME FEELING
LIKE I'M NEVER IN
CONTROL OF
ANYTHING!

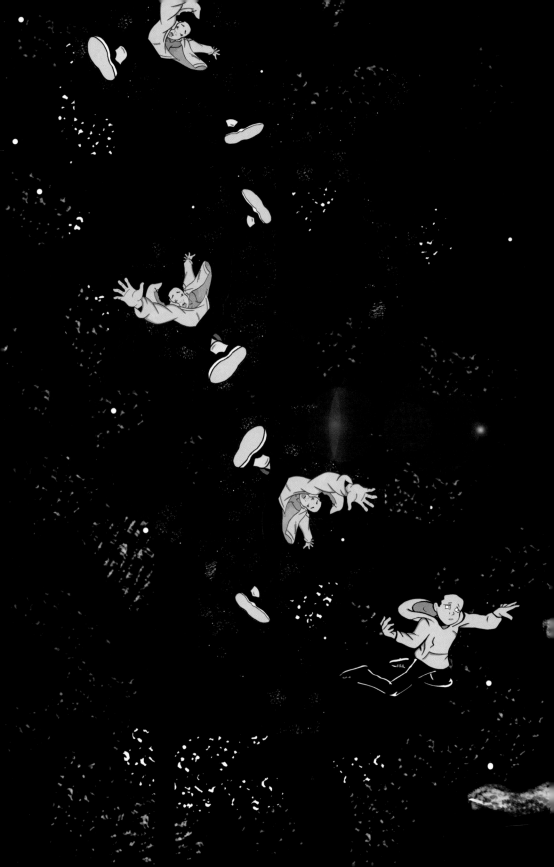

3:10

(GASP!) . . . WHERE DID I LEAVE MY *SKETCHBOOK?!!*

211

CHAPTER 13
THE FARCE AWAKENS

Sticks and Stones May Break My Bones But at LEAST Get My Name Right!

I used to think that when someone called me a name, that was the worst thing ever!

FATHEAD!

But you know what? I can deal with "Fathead" because my head isn't really fat.

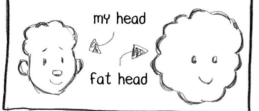

my head

fat head

or names like "Stinky" because I don't stink. (For the most part!)

show-off!

I've even gotten used to Shorty, Oreo, Light (which is short for light-skinned), and a thousand other names that I've been called.

la la la la

Because most times those names come from insecure people who want me to feel as bad about myself as they do about themselves.

BUT HOW CAN I BE ATTACKING THE SCHOOL IF ALL THIS STUFF *REALLY* HAPPENS?

I MEAN, NO OFFENSE, BUT YOU CALL DREW BY THE WRONG NAME *ALL THE TIME.*

AND THE YEAR IS ALMOST OVER.

AND SOME KIDS *DO* LOOK DOWN ON KIDS ON FINANCIAL AID.

AND KIDS *STARE.*

ALL THE TIME!

IT'S NOT ALWAYS EASY BEING SO DIFFERENT!

BUT JORDAN, BEING DIFFERENT IS A BLESSING. IT'S WHAT MAKES YOU SPECIAL.

I'M TIRED OF BEING SPECIAL!

BEING SPECIAL *STINKS!*

YOU AND DREW SHOULD BE PROUD TO BE HERE. I KNOW *I AM.*

JUST EMBRACE THE SCHOOL AND ALLOW IT TO EMBRACE YOU BACK.

I JUST WANT YOU TO BE HAPPY, JORDAN.

CHAPTER 14

RAD MEN

AND SPEAKING OF SUPERHEROES, DON'T FORGET MY PERSONAL PROTECTOR. JORDAN BANKS, DEFENDER OF THE UNIVERSE!

MILD-MANNERED CARTOONIST BY DAY. BLOODTHIRSTY VIGILANTE BY NIGHT.

AH, JEEZ! NOT *THIS* AGAIN.

C'MON, IT'S TIME FOR LUNCH.

FOR REAL, THOUGH. YOU GOT MY TWO-WEEK SUSPENSION DOWN TO A STUDY HALL.

AND DON'T FORGET THAT JORDAN *ALSO* GOT A STUDY HALL.

YEAH, WHO KNEW WE'RE NOT ALLOWED TO CLIMB ON TABLES AND SCREAM?

JORDAN BANKS IS NOBODY'S PUPPET!

PUPPET? *HMMM* . . .

I'LL MEET YOU GUYS AT LUNCH, THERE'S SOMETHING I GOTTA DO.

ANOTHER RESCUE MISSION, BATMAN?

HOPEFULLY.

228

229

THERE YOU ARE, JORDAN!

UH-OH!

WHEN I TOLD YOU THAT YOU COULD TELL *ONE* PERSON, I *ASSUMED* IT WOULD BE DREW OR LIAM.

BUT YOU KNEW *ASHLEY* WOULD TELL *EVERYONE!!!* PRETTY SMART.

AT FIRST, I WAS SO MAD I WANTED TO BEAT YOU UP . . .

UMM . . . I THINK THE SCHOOL HAS A "NO-BEAT-UP POLICY."

THEN, WHEN I REALIZED YOU DID THIS TO TRY TO HELP ME . . .

I WANTED TO GIVE YOU A HUG.

I'M PRETTY SURE THERE'S A "NO-HUGGING POLICY," TOO.

THEN I'LL JUST SAY THANKS.

UNLESS THERE'S A POLICY ON *THAT*, TOO!

NAH, THAT'S COOL.

To my family, Jay, Aren, and Autier.
Thank you for making me a better person.

Thanks to my agent, Judy Hansen,
my editor, Andrew Eliopulos, and Rosemary Brosnan
and the team at HarperCollins for embracing my vision.

Thanks to Marva Allen, Pam Allyn, Debra Lakow
Dorfman, David Saylor, Andrea Davis Pinkney,
and Andrea Colvin for inspiring me along the way.

Special thanks to my amazing colorist, Jim Callahan,
and to Jacqueline Woodson, Jeff Kinney, and Kwame Alexander
for your kind words and inspiration.

And last but not least, thanks to Barbara Slate,
Jim Keefe, Ray Billingsley, M'shindo Kuumba,
Eric Velasquez, Danni Ai, and Jennifer Crute
for making me a better artist.